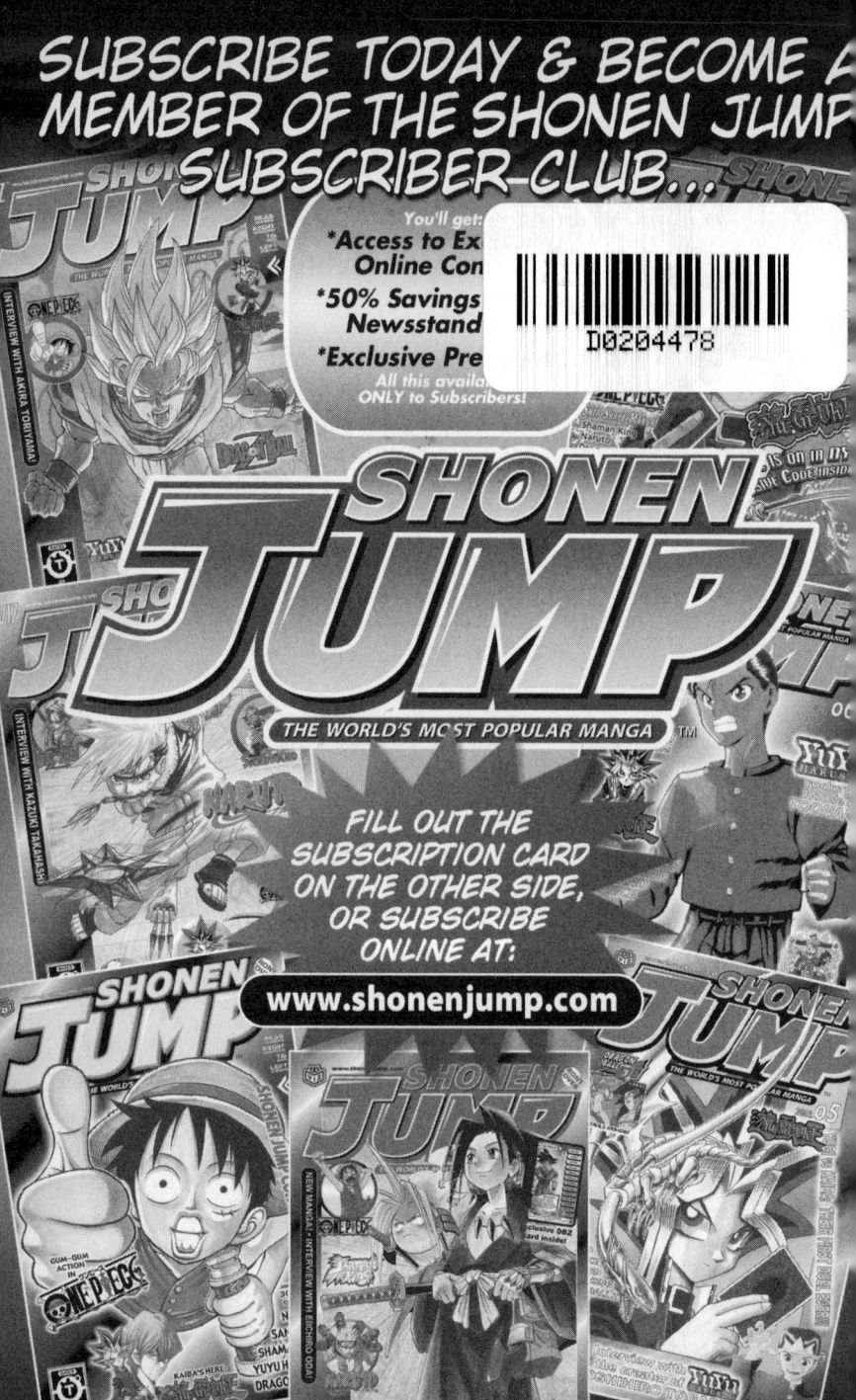

Tell us what you SHONEN JUMP manga!

Our survey is now available online.
Go to: www.*SHONENJUMP*.com/mangasurvey

Help us make our product offering better!

THE REAL ACTION
STARTS IN...

SHONEN JUMP
THE WORLD'S MOST POPULAR MANGA
www.shonenjump.com

ST ADVANCED

ST

viz media

CH

KOBAYA-KAWA...

...and fighting in his own name,

SENA!!

YOU'RE THE REAL DEAL NOW.

YOU'RE A REAL FOOTBALL PLAYER.

EYESHIELD 21

Volume 18

On sale February 2008!!

RUNNING AWAY? WRONG! I'M GONNA BEAT HIM!

I WANT TO KEEP AT IT. ON THE FOOTBALL TEAM!

IT'S JUST THAT... I'M NOT HERE TO TRY OUT...

THROWING OFF THE MASK...

LIGHT-SPEED RUNNING BACK...

YOUR CODENAME WILL BE... EYESHIELD 21!!!

I'M REALLY JUST A GOPHER WHO'S BEEN MADE INTO A FALSE HERO BUT... I'LL TRY TO DO THE BEST I CAN.

NOTRE DAME JUNIOR HIGH IN AMERICA...

...HE WAS THE ONLY JAPANESE WHO PLAYED AS AN ACE.

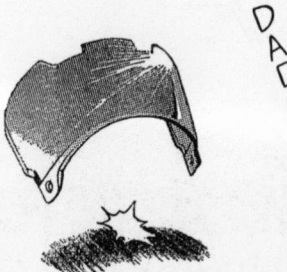

DADONK

Story by: Riichiro Inagaki

Art by: Yusuke Murata

Chief: Akira Tanaka

STAFF: Takahiro Hiraishi   Kentaro Kurimoto
Akira Nishikawa   Yukinori Kawaguchi
Masayuki Shiomura   Lee Sangmi

Uncover Hiruma's weakness.

S.K., Osaka prefecture

WELL...LI'L DB! I'LL LEAVE THIS TO YOU!
I DON'T WANNA DIE!

BOSS, YOU DEMON!!

I came up with something inconceivable.

Anabebe, Shizuoka Prefecture

Mamori losing it

Sena has a
disgusting smile

UGH?!
I MEAN...UUUUGH?!!

Has Yoichi Hiruma ever killed a human?

M.A.

SHOCK

NO WAY!!!

I'M SORRY THAT THERE ARE MANY UNSOLVED
ORDERS LIKE THESE, BUT WE'LL MAKE SURE
TO READ ALL OF THEM! SO SEND MORE,
EVERYBODY. YAHA!!

Unsolved Orders 021

I can't get TV Tokyo where I live so I can't watch the *Eyeshield 21* anime. Now I have a question. What do you think about 30 of us going to the TV station and threatening them to broadcast it?

Rui Hanazuki, Aomori prefecture

I'M SCARED!

YOU'RE GONNA GET ARRESTED!!

Is the gun that appeared in chapters 129 and 130 an M98F? It's a typical military handgun used in the world's strongest military, the U.S. forces (Army, Navy, Air Force, Marines), am I right? It's called an M9 in the Army, and it was formally adopted in 1985 after passing a strict handgun trial. Now it's being used worldwide. You can see it in games and movies, and it is the most famous handgun in the whole world, isn't it?

Yontana, Kagawa Prefecture, and others

SO DETAILED!!

WHAT'S GOING ON, HERE?
THIS CALLER'S QUESTION IS ITS OWN ANSWER!!

VVWOOM

End of Volume 17:
Drive to Be the Best

NO, NO, THAT'S NOT WHAT THE BIG DEAL IS...!

HE CALLED HIS GUITAR "THIS GUY"!!

HE SAID "THIS GUY"!

YOU GUYS SURE MADE A BIG DEAL OUT OF THAT...

SORRY.

I DIDN'T WANT THIS GUY TO GET BROKEN.

...HE JUST LAID OUT...

...KURITA ...?!!

WITH THAT SLENDER BODY...

SENA.

KOBAYA-KAWA.

INTERESTING.

ARE YOU ALSO EYESHIELD 21?

AHH! HE'S RUNNING TOWARD BANDO'S BENCH...

WATCH OUT!!

!!!

DADUMMMB

YOU JUST GOT IT?

...WE FIGHT EITHER OJO OR BANDO FOR 3RD PLACE.

MAN, HE'S SO SLOW!!

AND IF WE WIN, WE CAN STILL GO TO THE KANTO TOURNAMENT?!

AH!

THAT ...

...MEANS...

BWOOSH

HOORAY!

IT'S STILL NOT OVER YET!!

WHAT?

THE GAME'S OVER BUT THERE'S STILL SOMETHING'S GOING ON.

BOM BOM BOM   BOM BOM   AAAUGH!

TREMBLE

TREMBLE

TREMBLE

...**THAT JERK!**

WHY'S AN ATHLETE PLAYING A GUITAR IN THE STADIUM?!

I HAVE NO CLUE.

BESIDES...

BUT WHAT CONCERNS ME EVEN MORE IS...

...IT'S OBVIOUS THAT HE'S INCREDIBLY GOOD.

EYES?
...

RED
...

WINCE

IT'S THE OJO WHITE KNIGHTS!

NOW IN THE AFTERNOON...

...WE WILL FINALLY HAVE THE OTHER SEMIFINAL MATCH.

YOU STILL DON'T GET IT?

IN THE END...

...WHAT... HAPPENED?

HIRUMA DOESN'T...

...SHOW US THE RESULTS FOR THE OTHER BLOCKS.

WHO'S FACING OJO?

THE TEAM COMING FACE-TO-FACE WITH OJO IS...

...A TEAM THAT KEEPS MIRACULOUSLY WINNING—

SHF

THEY'RE RANKED AS CLASS-A IN THIS MONTHLY FOOTBALL MAGAZINE.

IT SAYS THEY'RE SUPER STRONG.

IT'S PROBABLY THIS GENSHIJIN DOO-DAH TEAM, DON'T YOU THINK?

WE HAVE TO CLAW OUR WAY UP.

WE'RE DEFINITELY GOING TO THE KANTO TOURNA-MENT...

...THIS TIME FOR SURE...

ooo

...EYE-SHIELD MASK?

HOW LONG ARE YOU GOING TO WEAR THAT...

SENA.

CLAP CLAP

THANK YOU VERY MUCH!!

CLAP CLAP CLAP

CLAP CLAP

CLAP CLAPCLAP

...THE DEIMON DEVIL BATS' TARO RAIMON.

THAT'S THE FIRST PERSON TO BEAT TETSUMA IN A CATCHING BATTLE...

HE WANTED TO HAVE A SHOW-DOWN...

...WITH HIM IN THE KANTO TOURNA-MENT...?

...ACTED ON HIS OWN.

TETSUMA...

MR. TETSUMA...

OH, I SEE!

...I WAS SAVED...!

BECAUSE HE STOPPED ME WITH THAT KNEE TACKLE...

WHO TOLD TETSUMA TO DO THAT?

WHO WAS IT?

NO ONE TOLD HIM.

NOPE.

...TO THE CHRISTMAS BOWL...!

WE'LL BE ABLE TO GO...

KACHACHING

SO YOU SEE...

I'LL BLAST HOLES IN YOUR BONES 'TIL YOU DIE!!

DIE A MILLION DEATHS!

BRRRIIIIIIIIIP

WHEEEEEN

...WHEN THIS QUADRUPLE-DAMN MONKEY PICKED A FIGHT WITH THE REFEREE...

...HE ALMOST GOT SUSPENDED AND THEN THERE'D BE NO WAY WE COULD WIN!

OO OO OO OO OO OO !!

AND ...

...THOSE EIGHT SCHOOLS ARE...

THIS HOMEPAGE IS SO CUTE...

AND THE FINAL 8TH SPOT IS...

HOKKAIDO 1ST PLACE.

SHIZUOKA 1ST PLACE.

TOKYO 1ST PLACE.

SIC DISTRICT 1ST PLACE.

KANAGAWA 2ND PLACE.

TOKYO 2ND PLACE.

KANAGAWA 1ST PLACE.

IT'S BECAUSE THERE'S SO MANY SCHOOLS IN TOKYO...

I SEE.

...TOKYO...

...3RD PLACE ...!!

...WE'LL BE IN THE THIRD-PLACE MATCH NEXT WEEK.

SINCE WE LOST IN THE SEMI-FINALS ...

...AND SLIDE INTO 3RD PLACE ...

IF WE WIN THEN...

POOF

I, MR. DEVIL BAT, WILL...

...TEACH YOU GUYS ABOUT THE KANTO TOURNAMENT!

YAAAA HAAAA!!

THIS IS THE CHRISTMAS BOWL SITE EVERYONE'S AIMING FOR.

TOKYO STADIUM!

FIRST, TAKE A LOOK AT THIS!

BAMPH!

Yes.

Yes.

MASTER! AN IDIOT LIKE ME WANTS TO KNOW...

...ADVANCE IN THE KANTO TOURNAMENT. HAIYA!

...EXACTLY HOW MANY TEAMS CAN...

AND FIGHTING FOR THAT HONOR ARE...

RUMBLE RUMBLE

ONLY ONE SCHOOL IN ALL OF KANTO CAN MAKE IT HERE!

TA-

DA

...THE STRONGEST EIGHT SCHOOLS FROM THE REGIONAL TOURNAMENT LEVEL.

THAT'S THE KANTO TOURNAMENT!!

CONSO-
LATION
...

...
MATCH
?!

WHAT'S...
THAT?

COME TO
THINK OF IT,
SHE'S ALWAYS
BEEN THE
ANALOG TYPE...

I'M NOT TOO
GOOD WITH
COMPUTERS...

JUST A
SEC.

HEY DAMN
MANGER,
OPEN OUR
PAGE!

Umm.

WHAT?

YOU
HAVEN'T
TOLD THEM
HOW THE
TOURNA-
MENT
WORKS?

DAMN
STRAIGHT.

IF THEY KNEW
BEFOREHAND,
THEY WOULD'VE
LIGHTENED UP.

V-Bowl

Shooting gallery, freestyle!!

...IF IT WEREN'T FOR TETSUMA, OUR BUTTS WOULD'VE BEEN TOAST.

HEH HEH HEH.

I DON'T KNOW WHY HE HELPED US BUT...

THUMP

...TET-SUMA.

...THANK YOU TO...

LATER, SAY...

THE CONSOLATION MATCH.

THIS IS OUR BONA FIDE LAST CHANCE.

AH!

HUH...?!

HEY! WHAT DID YOU DO THAT FOR, TETSUMA!!

KNEE...

...TACKLE?!

?!!

I WON'T LET A CLOWN LIKE YOU...

...END IT ALL ON SOME RULE THAT NOBODY KNOWS.

I'LL BE DAMNED IF I LET YOU END IT HERE!!

WE'RE GOING TO THE CHRISTMAS BOWL!

STOP MESSING AROUND, DAMMIT!!

YOU STU...

READ THE RULEBOOK!

IT'S WRITTEN THERE, RIGHT?

I GOT THE BALL!

FWIP

I GOT IT!!

I WON!

I HAVEN'T LOST YET!

UNTIL THE FINAL LINEUP ... ...THE GAME IS NOT OVER.

...I'D BECOME THE GREATEST CATCHER.

I PROMISED MR. HONJYO THAT...

SHUT UP!

SEE? I REALLY WON!!

YOU THINK YOU CAN END IT?!

DAMN, DAMN, DAMN ...!!

DAMN ...

DAMN ...

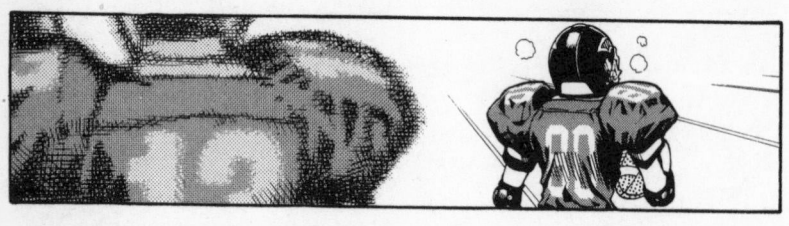

I GOT IT...

THE BALL...

I GOT IT.

...WHAT'RE YOU TALKING ABOUT?

ROARR

...GIVING UP!

NO-BODY'S...

LET'S DEFINITELY MAKE IT...

...TO THE CHRISTMAS BOWL!!

IS IT?

IS IT?

...ALL...

IT'S...

...OVER...

30

RAH RAH

Seibu Wild Gunmen **44** — Deimon Devil Bats **42**

VERY CLOSE ...

... DEIMON ...

I'LL BE WAITING FOR YOU AT THE FINALS.

A LOSS IS A LOSS.

IT DOESN'T MATTER WHETHER IT'S A 100-POINT OR A ONE-POINT DIFFERENCE.

RAH

THE NATIONAL HIGH SCHOOL FOOTBALL CHAMPIONSHIP TOKYO TOURNAMENT...

THE DEIMON DEVIL BATS...

...LOSE IN THE SEMI-FINALS!!

PLOP

AHH. THAT WAS CLOSE.

THAT WAS TOO CLOSE...!!

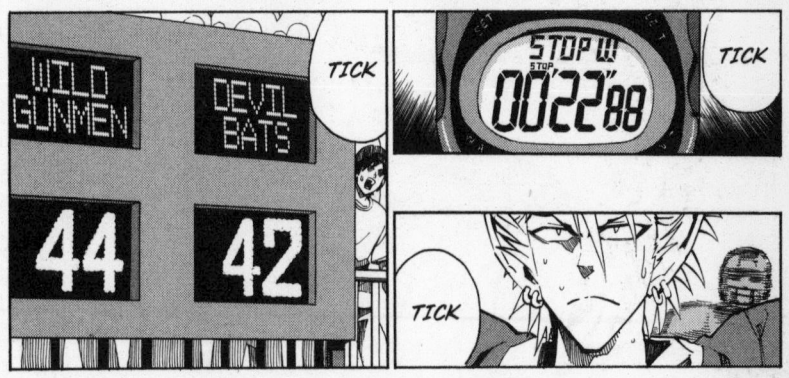

WILD GUNMEN — 44
DEVIL BATS — 42

STOP W
STOP
0'0'22"88

TICK

TICK

STOP W
STOP
0'0'00"00

TI-

CK

WATER RESISTANT

ALTHOUGH BOTH PLAYERS HAD POSSESSION OF THE BALL, THE MOMENT TETSUMA'S SHOULDER TOUCHED THE GROUND...

...FOR THE RECEIVING TEAM, SEIBU!

...IT WAS DETERMINED A CATCH AND DOWN...

DIDN'T MONTA...

...GET IT...?

WH-WH...

WHY...?

POSSESSION GOES TO...

THIS MEANS THE PLAY ENDED AT THAT POINT.

...THE SEIBU WILD GUNMEN!!

PAPAPAPAPA

HUH
...?

HE GOT IT!!

ALL RIGHT !!

HE REALLY... DID IT!

HE DID IT.

OPEN UP A PATH FOR MONTA!!

EVERYBODY TO THE FRONT AND BLOCK!!

TO THE FRONT!

IF IT COMES TO PHYSICAL STRENGTH...

IF WE... GET THIS...

...IT'S TETSUMA'S BALL!!

...ADVANCES TO THE FINALS...!!

WHOEVER WRESTLES IT AWAY...

!!

...ON THE BALL'S...

...LACES...?!

HIS FINGERS ARE...

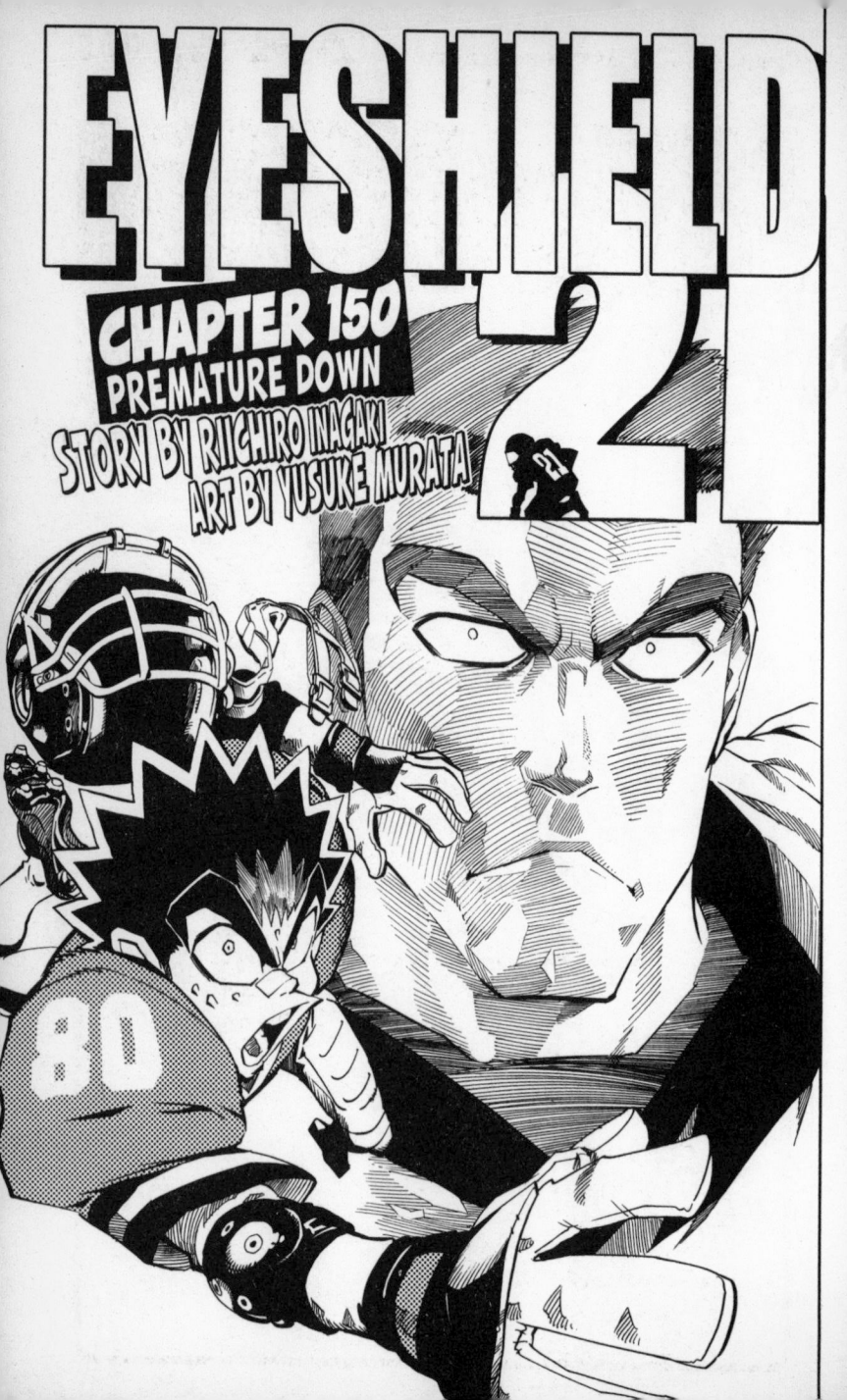

EYESHIELD 21

CHAPTER 150
PREMATURE DOWN

STORY BY RIICHIRO INAGAKI
ART BY YUSUKE MURATA

Investigation File #055

Uncover their love affairs!

ARE RUI HABASHIRA AND MEGU TSUYUMINE GOING OUT?

IF SO...SOB SOB SOB SOB...

Y.T., Chiba prefecture

HMPH. WHEN YOU'RE A KID, SEE.
YOU ALWAYS THINK A MAN AND A WOMAN CAN FALL IN LOVE JUST BY BEING TOGETHER.
YOU'LL UNDERSTAND BETTER WHEN YOU GET OLDER, YOUNG LADY.
WITH A MAN AND A WOMAN, FIGURING OUT WHETHER THEY'LL BE TOGETHER OR NOT ISN'T HALF AS EASY AS IT SOUNDS.
THERE'S THE EGO, THE BODY, PASSION, AND BONDS. THERE ARE JUST SO MANY THINGS THAT ONLY THOSE TWO CAN UNDERSTAND.
IN FACT, THERE SO MANY THINGS THAT THEY THEMSELVES CAN'T UNDERSTAND...

I DON'T REALLY GET IT BUT HE'S A GROWN-UP!
THIS GUY IS DEFINITELY A GROWN-UP!

Send your queries for Devil Bat 021 here!!

Devil Bat 021
Shonen Jump Advanced/Eyeshield 21
c/o VIZ Media, LLC
P.O. Box 77010
San Francisco, CA 94107

PLEASE BE PATIENT !!

WE CAN'T ANSWER EVERY QUERY ...

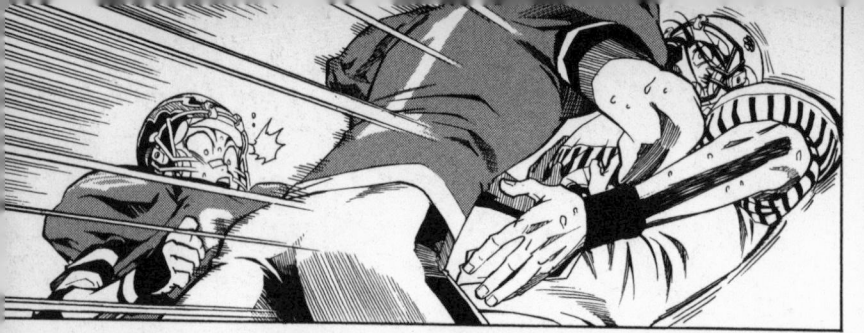

MON...
...TA...!!!

TETSUMA!!

YO!

DON'T MAKE ANY MISTAKES, DAMN OLDIE!

HERE WE GO.

ARE YOU GUYS READY?

PLEASE...

...GET IT...

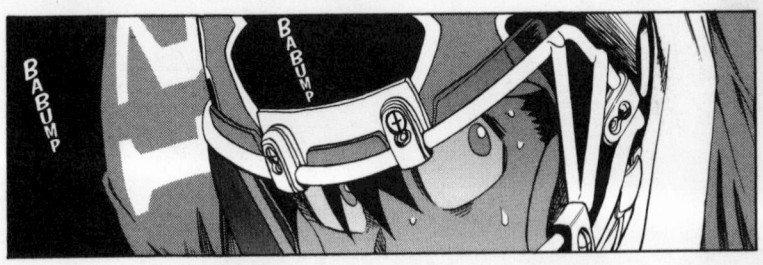

IT'S THEIR LAST CHANCE...!

THOSE THREE ARE FINALLY TOGETHER.

THEY'RE SENDING OUT ALL THEIR STARS!

DEFENSE AND OFFENSE DON'T MATTER ANYMORE.

SHF

SHF

OHHH. SEIBU'S THINKING THE SAME THING...

THE KID, TETSUMA, RIKU... USHIJIMA!!

THIS ONSIDE KICK WILL DECIDE THE OUTCOME OF THIS BATTLE!!

OF COURSE!

THE ONE WHO GETS IT...

...WILL BE...

...FROM EACH TEAM WILL FIGHT OVER THE BALL...

ELEVEN PLAYERS...

HA!

SO IT'S THAT SIMPLE.

...THE WINNER...!!

AN ONSIDE KICK IS...

... A DEADLY KICKOFF TECHNIQUE.

ALL WE CAN DO IS AN ONSIDE KICK.

...KICK THE BALL AS DEEP AS POSSIBLE INTO THE ENEMY'S TERRITORY, RIGHT?

USUALLY ON KICK-OFF WE...

...KICK THE BALL RIGHT INTO THE ENEMY'S FRONT LINE!

BUT ON AN ONSIDE KICK WE...

BATTLE???

A CAVE...

...MAN'S...

THE GAME WILL END THE MOMENT...

...THE BALL FALLS INTO SEIBU'S HANDS!

WHAT?!!

WITH JUST OVER 60 SECONDS LEFT!

...TO KICK NEXT... THEN IT'LL BE SEIBU'S BALL, RIGHT?

B-B-BUT IT'S OUR TURN...

SEIBU DOESN'T HAVE TO DO ANYTHING FOR 25 SECONDS ON EACH OF THEIR THREE PLAYS...

THAT'S RIGHT.

...TO EAT UP THE REST OF THE REMAINING TIME.

IT MEANS WE'RE DEFINITELY GONNA LOSE!!!

THEN WHAT ARE WE GONNA DO?

IRONI-CALLY...

THE BEST PLAY-MAKER IS...

...YOICHI HIRUMA.

I GUESS I WAS RIGHT.

THIS...

...ONE PLAY WILL DECIDE IT.

THE BEST PLAY-MAKER IS...

...THE ONE WHO WINS!

ARE YOU CRAZY?

THIS IS THE ONE PLAY...

HEH HEH HEH.

YOU KNOW IT.

...THAT WON'T NEED EITHER A PLAY-MAKER OR STRATEGY.

IT'LL JUST BE A PRIMITIVE BATTLE...

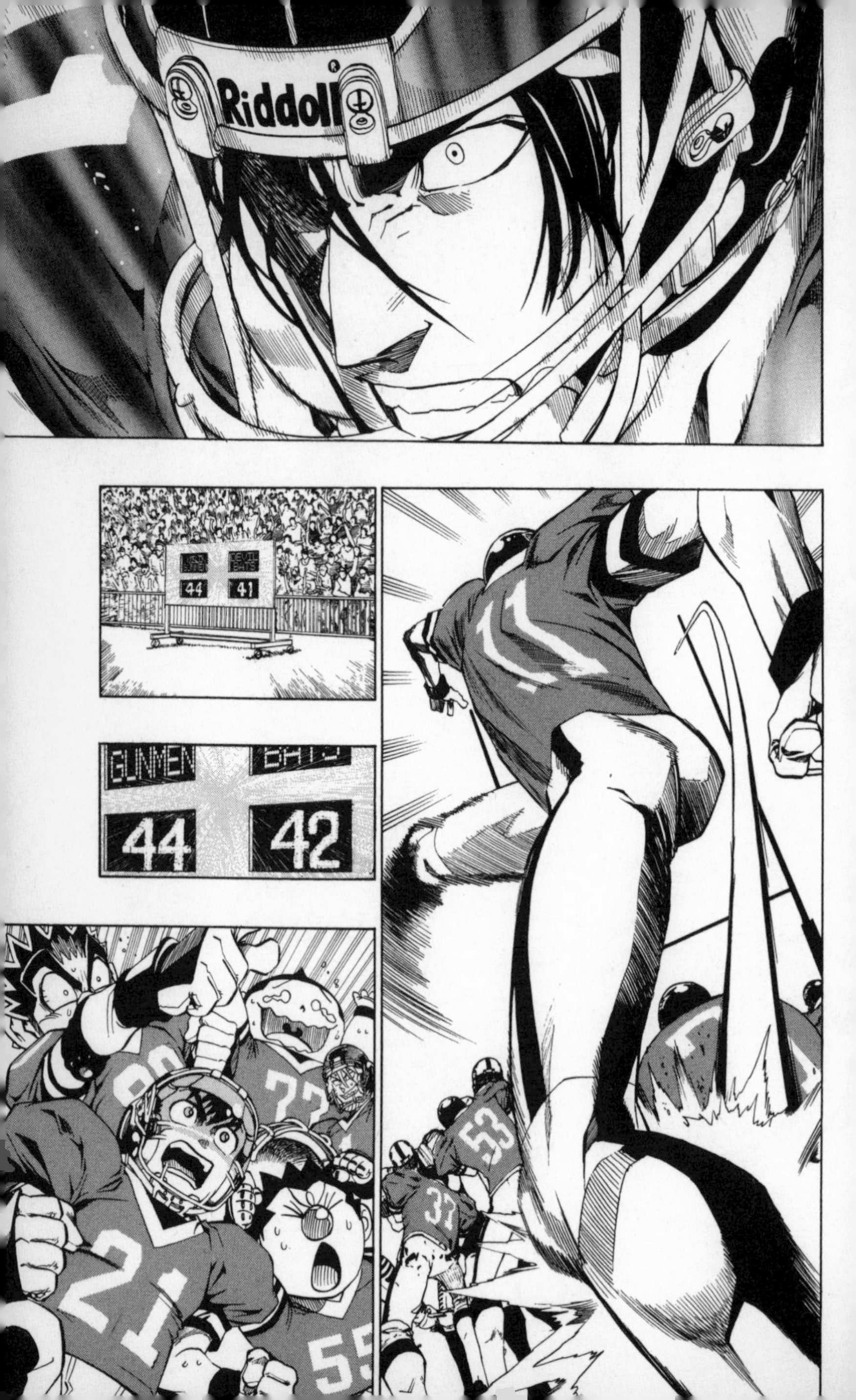
Riddoll
44
41
GUNMEN
44
42

Investigation File #054

An Order for a Personality Switch Simulation Experiment!!

I WONDER WHAT LIFE WOULD BE LIKE FOR SENA IF HIRUMA AND MAMORI SWITCHED PERSONALITIES. PLEASE CONDUCT THIS BIG EXPERIMENT!!

Caller

Kazunchi, Kanagawa Prefecture

YAHA! I'VE CREATED A MAMORI ROBOT AND A HIRUMA ROBOT WITH REVERSED PERSONALITES!

HEY SENA, GO GET A MILLION CREAM PUFFS FROM KARIYA!!

WHAT?! M-MAMORI'S...

HEH HEH HEH. DON'T PUSH AROUND THE DAMN PIPSQUEAK!! HERE'S A MACHINE GUN FOR YOU, DAMN PIPSQUEAK.

ACKK!! THAT'S MUCH SCARIER!!

THANK GOD IT'S THE OTHER WAY AROUND...

Chapter 149 A Primitive Battle

...EYE-SHIELD 21!

ONE MINUTE LEFT IN THE GAME!

THE ONE WHO FINALLY BEAT RIKU'S RODEO DRIVE IS...

Chapter 149 A Primitive Battle

...TOUCH-DOWN!!!

A MIRACU-LOUS...

V-Bowl

Extra down 02

The day the game arrived at Ojo.

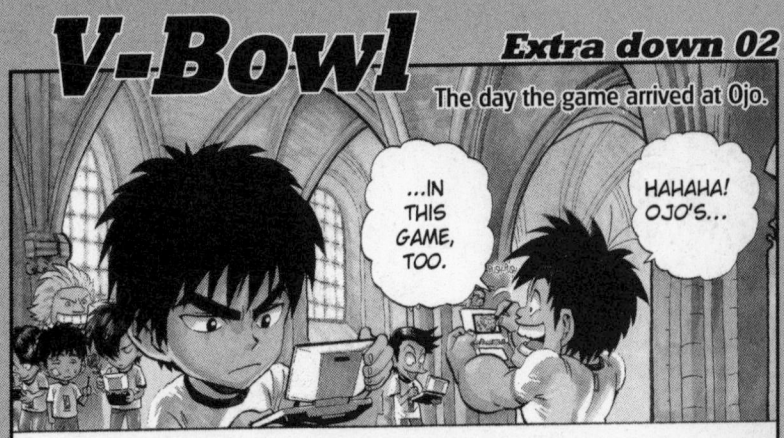

HAHAHA! OJO'S...

...IN THIS GAME, TOO.

WHOAAA! THERE'RE SO MANY THINGS I COULD POINT OUT, BUT I DON'T KNOW WHERE TO START!

YEAH, AMAZING!

AMAZING BUT...

IT HAS NOTHING AT ALL TO DO WITH THE GAME.

HUFF

HUFF

SOME-THING'S WRONG WITH THIS GAME.

NOOO. THAT'S WHY I SAID NOT TO GIVE SHIN ANY MACHINES!!

THE TOUCH-PEN IS OKAY.

IT'S NOT A MACHINE SO IT SHOULD BE FINE.

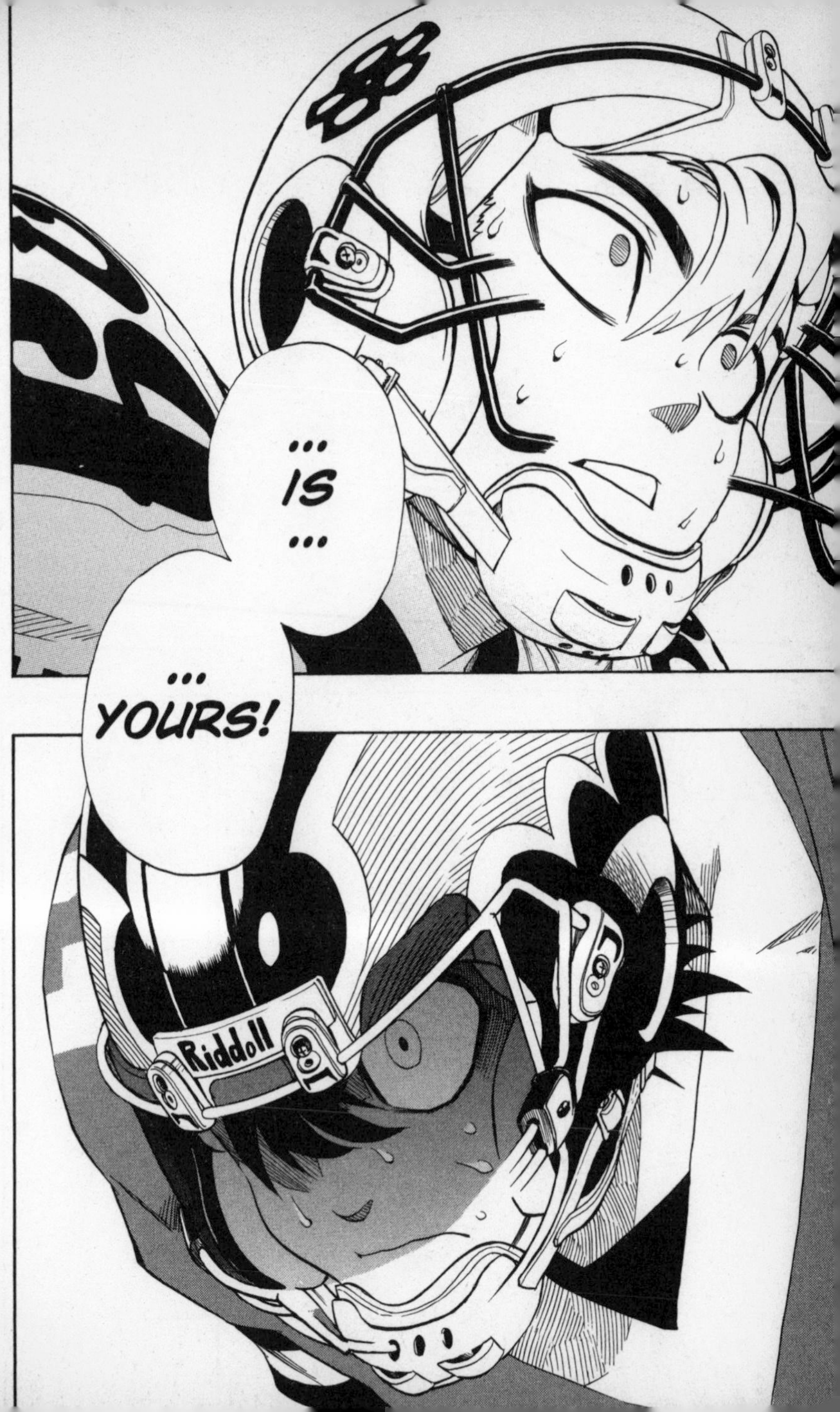
... IS ...
... YOURS!
Riddoll

TWIST AWAY WITH THE DEVIL BAT HURRICANE...!!

USE THE BODY AS A LEVER.

YOUR BODY'S THERE FOR THE BALL.

DON'T AVOID IT.

...SENA...

DASH AGAINST HIM AT FULL SPEED.

...OUR ...100TH BATTLE...

... THE ...

BALL ...!

YOU'VE GOT TO SACRIFICE YOURSELF ...

... FOR THE BALL.

... TAUGHT ME.

RIKU ...

BEFORE AND EVEN NOW.

GRAB

FACING ONE'S OPPONENT...

...HE'S A THREAT TO US YET.

I DON'T THINK...

...IT'S NOT SOMETHING TO RUN AWAY FROM.

IF I WANTED TO STEP OUT AND AVOID HIM...

...I WOULDN'T HAVE COME TOWARD RIKU IN THE FIRST PLACE.

THAT'S RIGHT. I CAME HERE ON MY OWN.

IT'S SINK OR SWIM!

I GOTTA GET BY HIM!

GET PAST ...!!

...WHO TAUGHT ME HOW TO RUN ...!!

EVEN THOUGH RIKU WAS THE ONE...

I'LL BEAT ...

... RIKU.

SHEEN!!

...THE LIGHT-SPEED RODEO DRIVE.

I'LL SHOW YOU...

I KNEW I COULDN'T ESCAPE IT, SO...

... WHY ...

HIS RODEO DRIVE ...

... SUDDENLY GOT FASTER.

WHOA! HE'S SO FAST!

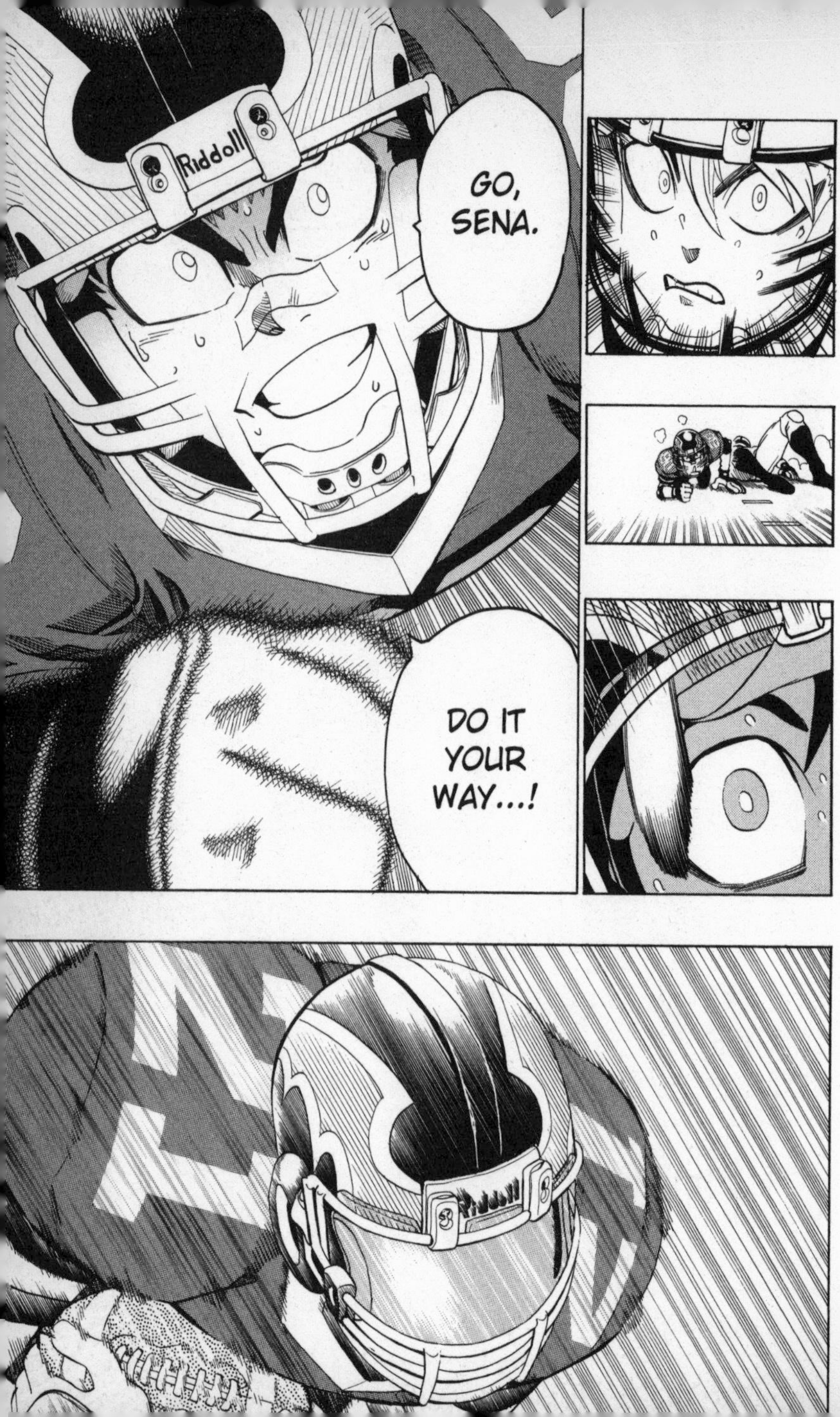
GO, SENA.
DO IT YOUR WAY...!

RIKU !!

SKIDDD

HE REALIZED IT AT THE LAST MINUTE!!

THAT MANIAC! GREAT JOB!

OHHH! RIKU'S ALREADY SNUCK AROUND!

THIS IS AS FAR AS I GO.

I'VE BEATEN...

I LEAVE THE REST TO YOU ALL...!!

...TETSUMA...!!

...GET THE...

...BALL.

DAMN! SOME-BODY...

NOOOOOO!!

THE BALL'S BEEN RIPPED...

...OUT OF TETSUMA'S HANDS?!

SLAP

Chapter 148
Light-Speed Crash

Investigation File #053

Uncover Doburoku's Sake!

DOBUROKU ALWAYS CARRIES A BOTTLE OF SAKE. WHAT KIND OF SAKE IS HE ALWAYS DRINKING?

Caller

Name withheld by request

NO, NOT AGAIN! THIS DATA GATHERING IS KILLING ME, I'M GONNA DIE!!

STOP COMPLAINING, YOU DAMN BAT! A SPY'S WORK IS ALWAYS HARD, YOU KNOW!

SAKE Malt SAKE Laojiu SAKE Brandy SAKE Cognac SAKE Bourbon SAKE Tennessee SAKE Awamori

SAKE Kokutou Shochu SAKE Shiso Shochu SAKE Soba Shochu SAKE Mugi Shochu SAKE Kome Shochu SAKE Imo Shochu

SAKE Grappa SAKE Mamushi SAKE Xinglujiu SAKE Rum SAKE Tequila SAKE Gin SAKE Vodka

SAKE Kirschwasser SAKE Chang SAKE Makgoli SAKE Blowfish Fin SAKE Rye SAKE Scotch

SAKE Moonshine SAKE Bubbly SAKE Booze SAKE Barley Pop SAKE Gunk SAKE Spirits SAKE Joy Juice

SAKE XXX SAKE Grog SAKE Popskull SAKE Rotgut SAKE Redeye

UWAAHH! SO MANY! THERE'S STILL A LOT MORE! YAHA!

MY GOODNESS. WHERE DOES THE OLD MAN HIDE ALL THAT SAKE?

...IS WHEN HE CATCHES THE BALL...

...AND TAKES IT INTO POSSES- SION.

THAT'S THE PRECISE MOMENT!!

...THE BALL.

FROM THE START...

...MY TARGET WASN'T...

MR. TET- SUMA.

HIS EYES AND MOVE-MENTS...

...AND THE BALL'S MOVE-MENTS!

FOLLOW THE KID!

DON'T LOOK AT TET-SUMA!

THAT'S WHY...

...IF YOU FOLLOW THE BALL...

THEIR COMBINATION IS PERFECT.

...MONTA'S INTERCEPTION OF THAT PASS...

...WAS OUR LAST CHANCE...

DAMN.

WE READ THE PASS BUT...

THERE'S NO WAY WE CAN INTERCEPT...

...SUCH A LOW AND FAST PASS...!!

MONTA!!

SAKE

A SUPER FAST SHOT?!

AN UNDER-HAND THROW...

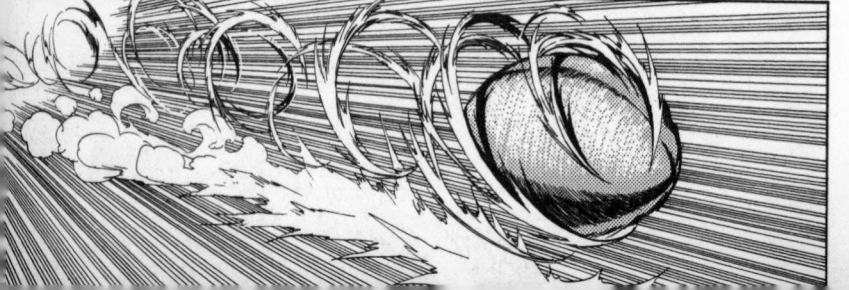

R OO AA

RIKU!!

WE'RE SET FOR THE FINALS!

TET-SUMA!!

GREAT, KID!!

HUT!!

BABUMP BABUMP

...FOR THE MOST PART, I CAN PREDICT THE BEST PATTERN HE'LL USE...

THAT'S WHY I CAN READ HIM.

...IN ORDER TO WASTE TIME.

IT'S NOT 100% BUT...

WITHOUT A DOUBT, HE'S WELL AWARE...

...OF THE SUCCESS RATE OF EVERY PASS.

"SHIEN MUSHA-NOKOJI" IS A GENIUS.

...WE USED MY "BLAST" TO ADVANCE...

THAT'S WHY IN THE SECOND HALF...

BOOM

I SEE... THE REAL BATTLE STARTS ONCE THE TIME STARTS RUNNING OUT!

...EVEN THOUGH IT USED A LOT OF TIME.

...AND THEY HAVE FEWER OFFENSIVE OPTIONS, RIGHT?

AS THE REMAINING TIME WINDS DOWN, THE TEAM IN THE LEAD GOES INTO A WINNING MODE...

NOW IS THE MOMENT...

...OF TRUTH FOR...

...TO READ...

...THIS PASS...?

ALL OF THAT...

...WAS PREPAR-ATION...

...CUTTING OFF THE PASS AND STEALING THE BALL...

...IS THE SHORT PATTERN PASS TO TETSUMA.

THE "HITCH."

ACCORDING TO SEIBU'S STATS TODAY...

...THE PLAY WITH THE HIGHEST RATE OF SUCCESS...

LET'S GO WITH THE SAFEST PATTERN.

A "HITCH" TO TETSUMA.

NOD

KID...!

...CAN'T BE UNPRE-PARED.

THAT CUNNING DEIMON PLAYMAKER, YOICHI HIRUMA...

SOME-THING'S NOT RIGHT.

...CONSUMING PLAYS AS WE PLEASE...

HE'S LETTING US USE OUR TIME...

IT'S GOING TOO SMOOTHLY.

LIKE I ALWAYS SAY.

SOME-THING'S UP FOR SURE...

NOTHING GOOD COMES OF THINGS GOING TOO SMOOTHLY.

WE STILL DON'T KNOW THE OUTCOME!!

RAT TAT TAT

OR MAYBE LIKE THAT SAFETY!

WE CAN CRUSH THEIR RUN...

...WE CAN INTERCEPT IT...

SNATCH

SEE? IF THEY MAKE A LONG PASS...

...GIVES US ANY... CHANCE...

THAT'S IF THEY GO FOR A PLAY THAT...

THAT'S PROBABLY THE ONLY PLAY THEY'LL USE.

SEIBU'S SPECIALTY IS THE KID'S QUICK-DRAW SHOTGUN.

ITS SHORT PASSES CAN'T BE INTERCEPTED.

WE'RE GOING TO PLAY IT SAFE FROM HERE ON OUT.

TWIRL TWIRL

THERE'S NOT ENOUGH TIME...!

QUICK!

WE HAVE TO GET BACK ON OFFENSE...!

YEAH.

THAT'S EXACTLY WHY THEY'RE TAKING THEIR TIME...

YOU'RE EATING UP ALL OF OUR TIME TO CATCH UP!!

WOOEEE! WHY ARE YOU GUYS TAKING SO LONG...!

JUST USE 25 SECONDS ON EACH PLAY...

...AND EAT UP THE LAST THREE MINUTES TO VICTORY!!

GA HA HA HA!

NATURALLY THE TEAM IN THE LEAD WILL USE UP EVERY SECOND.

THAT'S CALLED STRATEGY.

...YOU HAVE 25 SECONDS TO START EACH PLAY.

IN FOOT-BALL...

ROARRR

...COMES DOWN TO THE FINAL THREE MINUTES!

TOKYO'S STRONGEST SUPER OFFENSIVE BATTLE...

Chapter 147
FINAL TRAP, FINAL HUNT

ROARRR

SEIBU WILD GUNMEN...

FORTY-FOUR POINTS!

DEIMON DEVIL BATS...

THIRTY-FIVE POINTS!!

ROARR

Eyeshield 21 Survey Corner — **Devil Bat 021**

Investigation File #052

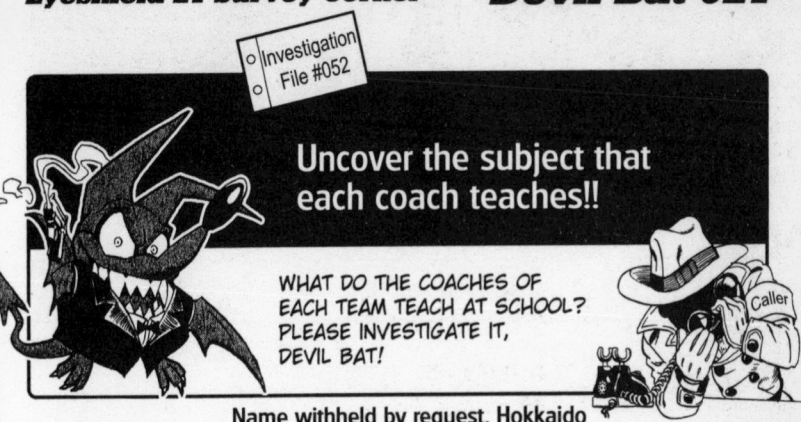

Uncover the subject that each coach teaches!!

WHAT DO THE COACHES OF EACH TEAM TEACH AT SCHOOL? PLEASE INVESTIGATE IT, DEVIL BAT!

Name withheld by request, Hokkaido

OH NO, BOSS! DO I HAVE TO GATHER DATA AGAIN? IT'S HARD BUT I'LL TRY. YAHA!

Shinryuji Nagas	Sengoku Samurais	Sankaku Punks	Seibu Wild Gunmen	Ojo White Knights
Sumito Sendoda	Mitsuhide Toyotomi	Saburota Sumi	Doc Horide	Gunpei Shoji
Subject	**Subject**	**Subject**	**Subject**	**Subject**
Zen meditation	Japanese History	Math	English	P.E.
Opinions from students in his class	Opinions from students in his class	Opinions from students in his class	Opinions from students in his class	Opinions from students in his class
We don't need this subject in high school.	Enough already! Can we please learn about something else besides the Sengoku Period?	I don't think triangles are the right shape for classroom hand-outs.	I know it's too late to say this but please don't let him bring firearms to class.	He is usually very strict but sometimes he strictly lets us see the strictness hiding behind his strictness.

MAN, NONE OF THEM ARE POPULAR...

JUST EAT UP THE TIME AND GET THROUGH THIS!

OK, OK!

THREE MINUTES LEFT! OK!

NOW IT'S BACK TO A NINE-POINT DIFFER-ENCE!!

WILD GUNMEN 44

DEVIL BATS 35

ROAR

...EVERY-THING'S BEEN SET UP FOR THIS MOMENT.

FROM THE MOMENT THE SECOND HALF STARTED...

HEH HEH HEH. NOT BAD.

DEFEND LIKE YOU'RE GONNA DIE, YOU DAMN CHUMPS.

THERE'LL ONLY BE ONE FINAL SHOT!!

THE CHANCE TO KILL THEM WILL COME!!

IT'S EXACTLY THE SAME ... ...AS THE KID'S LAST PLAY...!

THE KICK WAS A DECOY ...

TWO-POINT CONVER-SION!!

STRETCH

...GIVE UP!!

DON'T ...

TIME!

EAT UP THE TIME ANY WAY YOU CAN!

IT DOESN'T MATTER IF THEY SCORE A TOUCH-DOWN!

TWEEEET

BUMP BWUMP

WHOOSH

THE REMAINING TIME IS...

...SEVEN MINUTES...!

SO... IF IT'S A 17-POINT DIFFERENCE ...

THEY NEED TO SCORE THREE TOUCHDOWNS OR THEY WON'T CATCH UP!

THE MAX YOU CAN GET FROM A TOUCHDOWN IS EIGHT POINTS.

...THIS ISN'T GOOD.

THERE'S A BIG DIFFERENCE BETWEEN 16 AND 17 POINTS.

SCORING THREE TOUCHDOWNS IN SEVEN MINUTES...

...IS IMPOSSIBLE ...!

THEY DON'T SEEM TO HAVE ANY COUNTER FOR TETSUMA.

YOU DIDN'T PLAY IT SAFE.

YOU'RE GOING FOR THE KILL, EH?

AAAUGH!!

IT'S NOW A 17-POINT DIFFER-ENCE!!

WILD GUNMEN 44

DEVIL BATS 27

EVEN WITH THREE OF US, DAMN ...!!!

DAMN... NOT AGAIN...

RUARR

NOW WE'RE BACK WHERE WE STARTED...!

OH NO... IN THE SECOND HALF WE REDUCED THE GAP...

...FROM 20 TO EIGHT POINTS.

HIRUMA, MONTA AND EYESHIELD ARE...

...SURROUNDING HIM!!

DA-DUM

HIRUMA CAUGHT IT IN TIME!

ALL RIGHT!

!!

CHUG CHUG

...THE BEST RECEIVER!

TETSUMA IS...

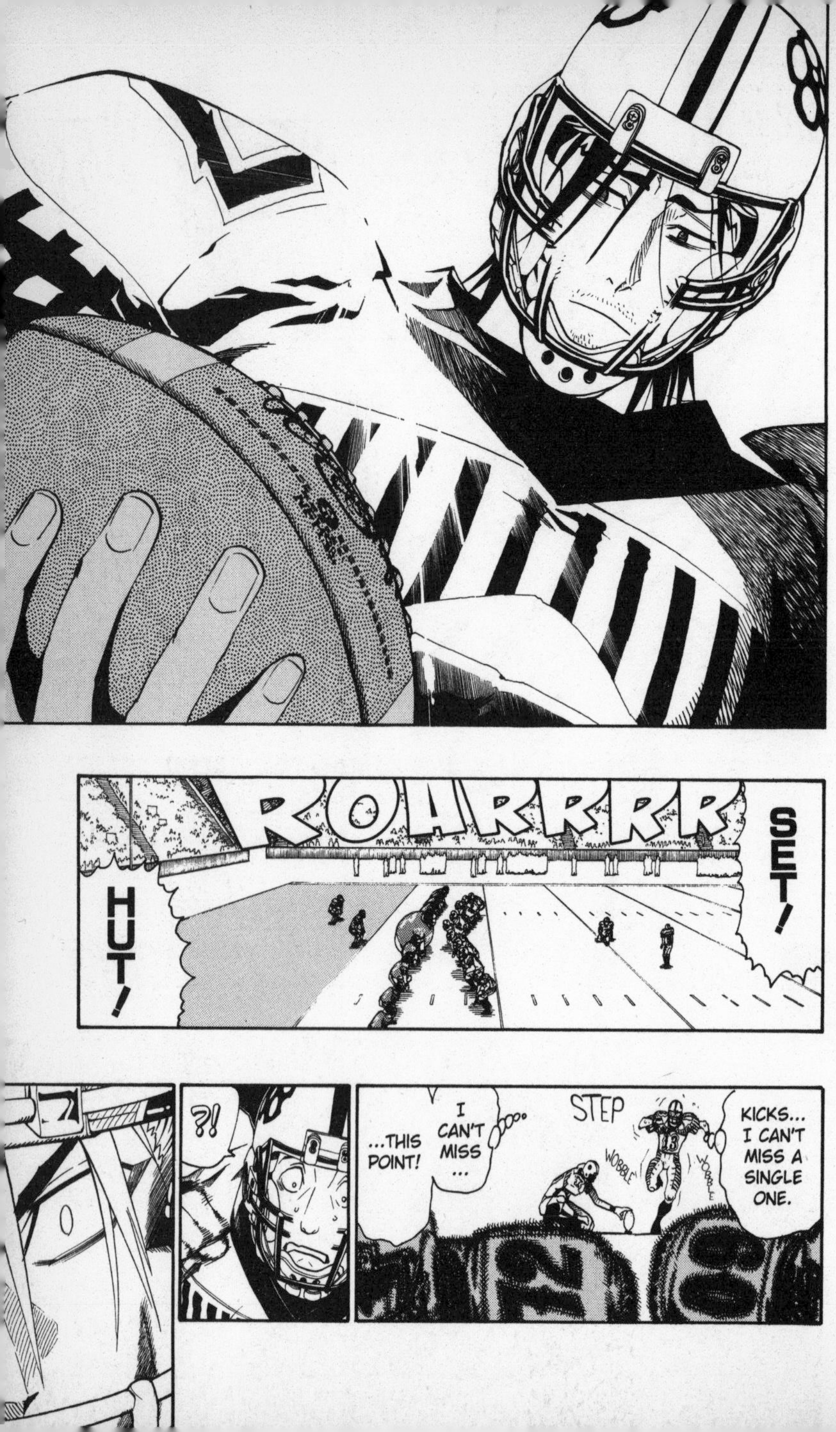

ROARRRR

HUT!

SET!

...THIS POINT!

?!

I CAN'T MISS...

STEP

WOBBL

KICKS... I CAN'T MISS A SINGLE ONE.

WE'RE ALL PLACING OUR HOPES IN YOU.

SHIEN.

NO MATTER WHAT!

I HAVE TO BE... NUMBER ONE.

NUMBER ONE...!!

I REMEMBER THE TIME WHEN I WOULD HAVE DIED TO GET THAT POSITION...

TO BE NUMBER ONE...

SO DON'T ACT SO COOL!

YOU'RE ACTUALLY BURNING UP INSIDE.

THE DRIVE TO...

...BE NUMBER ONE!!

CHRISTMAS BOWL!!

ZING ZING

NUMBER ONE...

GOLD MEDAL !!

POW

WOOOEEEE! WE ALMOST HAD 'EM!!

BARELY... HE GOT THE BALL IN.

TOUCH-DOWN!!

JUST A BIT MORE...

AND WE COULD'VE STOPPED SEIBU'S ATTACK...!

THEY'RE DETERMINED TO MAKE A COMEBACK...!!

...AGAINST TOKYO'S STRONGEST TEAM, SEIBU.

FROM A 23-POINT GAP...

THOSE DEIMON GUYS... ARE VERY SERIOUS.

THAT'S...

THEY'RE SIMILAR TEAMS BUT...

...THE STRENGTH THAT CAN ONLY COME FROM CLAWING YOUR WAY UP FROM THE BOTTOM.

...IF DEIMON HAS ONE ADVAN-TAGE...

THIS IS IT... FOR THE SEIBU WILD GUNMEN.

ROAR

STOP THEM!!

CRUNCHBANG

THE NEXT PLAY WILL BE THEIR LAST ATTACK!

FORCE YOUR WAY THROUGH, RIKU!

BUMP BUMP BUMP

WELL?! DID IT GO IN?!

WHOA!

THUDDD

FWSH

KKH

HRNGH!!

CRUNCH

WHAM CRASH

OOOOOOOOOOH

JUST IN FRONT ...

...OF THE GOAL LINE!!

THEY'VE GOT HIM DOWN!

THAT FACE IS EVEN MORE AWESOME!!

AWESOME!

USING HIS SHORT BODY TO LIFT THE OPPONENT FROM BELOW.

THE RIP!!

IT'S KOMUSUBI'S DEADLY TECHNIQUE...

ARE YOU PUMPED UP FOR THE GAME OR HAPPY FOR YOUR PUPIL? MAKE UP YOUR MIND.

YOU HAVE THE SWEETEST FACE! WHAT HAPPENED?!

AWESOME, KOMUSUBI!

NINE MINUTES AND 30 SECONDS LEFT!

DE...

DE...

...FENSE!

...FENSE!

...THERE'S NO WAY DEIMON CAN WIN.

ANYWAY... IF WE CAN'T STOP SEIBU'S SHOTGUN EVEN ONCE...

GROWAWRRR

GROWRRR

...AN EXAMPLE...

AN...

...WE'LL DEFINITELY STOP IT!!

IT'S SEIBU'S ATTACK. THIS TIME...

Chapter 146 The Drive to Be the Best

RAAH

DEIMON'S OFFENSIVE STRENGTH ...

...ISN'T THAT SOFT...!

BUT THAT DOESN'T STOP THE OTHERS.

THEY'RE MARKING ...

...EYE-SHIELD 21 HEAVILY.

SNATCH

TOUCH-DOWN!!

THAT'S WHY, SENA...
... I'LL ...
...NEVER LOSE!
I MAY BE ABLE TO WIN.
AGAINST THE ONE WHO TAUGHT ME HOW TO RUN.
AGAINST RIKU...!!

IT'S NOT A MATTER OF USING THE DEVIL BAT GHOST.

I JUST CAN'T TURN...!!

I CAN'T EVEN TELL WHEN HE'S GOING TO GO FOR THE TACKLE!

...IMPROVING, EVEN DURING MATCHES.

EYESHIELD 21...NO, SENA'S RUNNING IS...

I SHOULD'VE KNOWN.

ROARR

I SHOULD'VE SEEN IT.

NO, THAT'S IMPOSSIBLE, BUT...

IF I COULD BEAT THE RODEO DRIVE SOMEHOW...

...THAT WILL BE WHEN SENA HAS SURPASSED ME.

WHEN THE SCORE GOES FROM 99-0 TO 99-1...

STILL... IF I CAN FIND A WAY.

DO YOU REMEMBER, SENA?

BACK THEN... WHEN THE TWO OF US PRACTICED...

...THE CHASING GAME.

WITH JUST SPEED...

...YOU CAN GET RID...

...OF THOSE GUYS WHO PICK ON YOU.

YOU'RE PATHETIC, SENA.

YOUR FOOTWORK FOR THE STARTING DASH IS STILL OFF.

...WITH THAT LAST ONE...

...IT'S 98-0, YOU KNOW!

YEAH... I REMEM-BER.

I'D NEVER FORGET.

NOT EVEN ONCE... WAS I ABLE TO BEAT YOU.

TOUCH-
DOWN!!

WOOM

OH
...

... SHOOT!

‼️

THIS RODEO DRIVE...

DAMN! THIS IS A PROBLEM.

AMAZING! SUPER ACCELERATION TECHNIQUE!!

AH-

HEY, KID.

...IS THAT WHAT YOU SAID?

RIKU...

SENA... EYE-SHIELD 21...

CAN YOU LEAVE HIM TO ME?

...THAN AN AVERAGE FIRST-YEAR.

...HE'S GOT MORE GUTS...

JUST LIKE HIS RUNNING TECHNIQUE...

SEIBU WON'T ...

WE WON'T LOSE!

...AND I WON'T!!

FWSH

SNAP

CLACK
CLACK

SHOOSH

WE CAN'T AFFORD TO LOSE ONE CHANCE...!!

WHO'D A THOUGHT SEIBU WOULD BE DRIVEN INTO A CORNER SO QUICKLY...

WE... CAN'T AFFORD ANY MORE SCREW-UPS.

HUH? EH... HUH?

I CAN'T DO UP THE HELMET...

CLICK CLICK

HUH?

...SABO.

IT'S ALL RIGHT...

...

ROARRR

NOTHING GOOD EVER COMES...

...OF GETTING WORKED UP AND EXPECTING TOO MUCH...

●●●

IS IT REALLY THAT HARD TO SAY?

YOU'RE A HUMBLE GENTLEMAN AS ALWAYS.

●●●

THE FIRST HALF WAS TOO GOOD.

JUST AS I THOUGHT.

TSK, TSK, TSK. THIS ISN'T GOOD...

...IS NOTHING TO JOKE ABOUT.

THE PRESSURE OF BEING CHASED THIS FAR IN THE SECOND HALF...

BADUMP BADUMP BADUMP

NO ONE CAN MAKE US LOSE HOPE!

... NOT!

YOU MAY THINK I'M A MONKEY WHO GETS SHY AFTER BEING PRAISED BY THE ENEMY, BUT I'M NOT!

GEE, THANKS.

THAT COMEBACK DIDN'T EVEN SOUND HUMAN...

IS THAT ALL YOU WOOEEE ?!

NOD NOD

AT LEAST THE MONKEY PART'S TRUE.

HMM, WELL...

NO, NOT THAT.

THAT WAS JUST GIBBERISH ...

THE MONKEY PART?!

ABOUT THAT...

SO ...

... YOU'RE SERIOUS?

YOU MEAN THE CHRISTMAS BOWL ...

...EH?

ABOUT ... THAT ...?

Chapter 145
The Pursuer and the Pursued

FIELD GOAL KICK!!!

IT WENT IN!

Chapter 145 The Pursuer and the Pursued

Seibu gave up a safety!

It's an 11-point gap...

CHOK

They forced their way to the goal line ...

...and pushed back the enemy.

Ku-kurita and the three bastard brothers ...

No, it was all of the Devil Bats!

Since it was a safety... ...Deimon gets to attack again...!!

And that's not all, Suzuna.

o Investigation
o File #051

Uncover the nicknames given by Suzuna!!

I NOTICED THAT SUZUNA CALLS KURITA BY A NICKNAME. WHO ELSE DOES SHE CALL BY A NICKNAME?

Caller

Y.T., Toyama Prefecture and others

I WENT AHEAD AND GATHERED THEM HERE! YAHA!

Jumonji	**Monji**	Kuroki	**Krokky**	Togano	**Toga**
Komusubi	**Li'l Komusubi**	Yukimitsu	**Yukky**	Ishimaru	**Tetsu**
Cerberus	**Cujo**	Piggyberus	**Fatso**	Doburoku	**Fatso**

HEY!! MINE'S THE SAME AS THAT THING!

REAL MEN DON'T CRY...

NOT GOOD... THIS PRES- SURE!

THE WALL IS...

SEIBU... WILD GUNMEN.

SAFETY!!

WHUMP

THE POWER OF KICKING!

WITH THOSE THREE TOGETHER...

...BUT THE THREE OF THEM WERE THE DEAREST OF FRIENDS.

AT SCHOOL, THEY WERE OUTSIDERS...

...THEY'LL RIP SEIBU'S OFFENSIVE PATTERNS APART.

KURO-KI.

TOGANO.

°°°

OH!

JUMONJI'S IN SERIOUS MODE!!

FORGET ABOUT EVERYTHING ELSE.

WE'RE GOING TO CRUSH THE CENTER WITH EVERYTHING WE'VE GOT.

SHUF...

HERE COMES THE CENTER RUN!!

BOOM

000

WELL, THAT'S WHAT PEOPLE NORMALLY DO.

THEY GAVE UP ON THE SHOTGUN FORMATION.

I GUESS IT'S A RUN UP THE MIDDLE.

LOOKS LIKE THEY'RE GOING BY THE BOOK.

...YOICHI...

...HIRU-MA.

YOU'RE DAMN RIGHT!

IF IT WERE YOU...

...WOULD YOU HAVE GONE WITH THE SHOTGUN?

...BELIEVE IN THE STRENGTH OF YOUR FRIENDS...

BELIEVE IN THE BOOK OR...

COACH...

...TIME'S UP.

...

YOUR DECISION, PLEASE...

BABUMP...

TWEEEEET

ROARRR

THIS IS THE FIRST TIME...

...THAT SEIBU'S BEEN FORCED TO START FROM SUCH A DANGEROUS ZONE...

AWESOME KICK!!

BA BUMP...

BA BUMP...

IF THEY GO WITH THE KID'S SHOTGUN...

IF HE'S CAUGHT, IT'LL BE A SAFETY!

CRASH!

...THEY'LL BE THROWING FROM INSIDE THEIR OWN GOAL LINE.

HEH HEH HEH... WELL...

WHICH ONE WILL THEY USE?

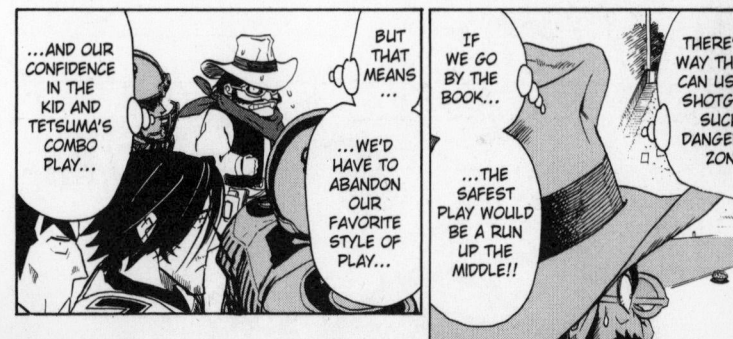

...AND OUR CONFIDENCE IN THE KID AND TETSUMA'S COMBO PLAY...

BUT THAT MEANS...

...WE'D HAVE TO ABANDON OUR FAVORITE STYLE OF PLAY...

IF WE GO BY THE BOOK...

...THE SAFEST PLAY WOULD BE A RUN UP THE MIDDLE!!

THERE'S NO WAY THAT WE CAN USE THE SHOTGUN IN SUCH A DANGEROUS ZONE!

SLUMP !!!

WE'RE SAVED ...

...ONLY A FEW CENTIMETERS AWAY FROM...

...THEIR OWN GOAL LINE!!

SEIBU'S POINT OF POSSESSION IS...

NOPE...

LOOK AT OUR POSITION.

TH...

THIS IS...!!

TIME OUT!

DASH

RIKU'S GOT IT!

IT'S SEIBU'S BALL!!

KCH

DDD

BUT... IT WAS CLOSE!

I KNEW IT! RIKU'S FAST, ALMOST! AND HE'S GOT SKILL!

THE MOST IMPORTANT PART OF A KICKOFF IS ITS HEIGHT!!

...THE EASIER IT IS TO SURROUND THE ENEMY.

THE LONGER IT TAKES THE BALL TO FALL BACK DOWN...

THAT'S WHAT MAKES A POWERFUL KICKOFF!!

SURE, EVEN I KNOW THAT.

IF IT'S ABOUT KICKING, I CAN TALK FOREVER!

NO THANKS!

HOW FAR IS IT GOING TO GO?!

THAT'S THE MOTHER OF ALL KICKS!!

HOW FAR?!

I'VE NEVER SEEN A KICK LIKE THIS IN HIGH SCHOOL...

FAR-THER...

BUT DEIMON'S KICKS HAVE ALWAYS BEEN SO SHORT!

THIS ONE'S GOING TO GO EVEN FARTHER!

FALL BACK, ISERI!

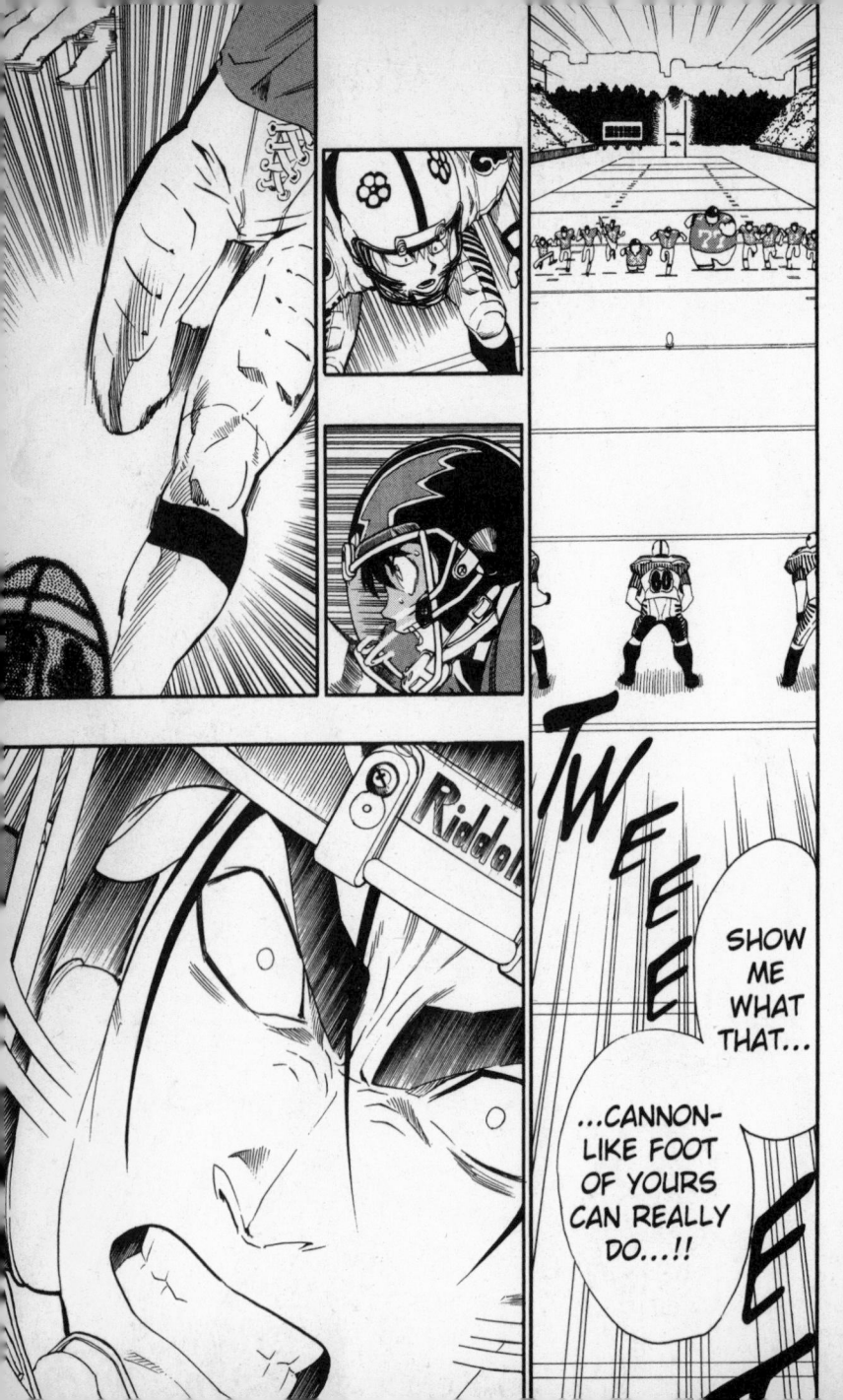

ON OUR KICKOFFS TODAY...

RIKKY RAN ONE IN FOR A...

...TOUCHDOWN RIGHT WHEN THE MATCH STARTED.

...HE MANAGED TO RUN HALF THE FIELD.

ON THE NEXT ONE...

ROARR

WITH THIS KICKOFF...

...I WONDER HOW MUCH DISTANCE WE'LL GET.

MUSASHI!

LET'S SEE JUST HOW COOL YOU ARE.

ROAR

THAT'S RIGHT...

...THIS IS MUSASHI'S FIRST KICKOFF...!

Chapter 144
The Devil Bats' Big Gun

THAT WON'T HAPPEN...

...USHI-JIMA.

...WON'T SCORE AT ALL IN THE SECOND HALF!!

YOU'RE ASSUMING THOSE GUYS...

BA-BUMP

ROARRR...

THERE'S STILL THE KID, TETSUMA, AND RIKU!!

IT'S OUR TURN TO ATTACK NOW.

JUST KEEP ON YAPPING.

EVEN IF IT'S JUST TWO TOUCH-DOWNS...

T-TWO MORE!

...THE TABLES WILL BE TURNED!!

TWO MORE TOUCH-DOWNS AND...

YEAH.

KRACKK

ONE MORE JOB...

...LEFT TO DO.

BUT...

...WITH THIS...

ROARR

DEIMON GETS ANOTHER SEVEN POINTS!

WILD GUNMEN 29

DEVIL BATS 16

NOW THE GAP IS 13 POINTS!!

...BETTER BE THE REAL THING WITH THE NEXT ONE.

HEH HEH HEH. WHATEVER.

THIS BIG GUN KICK SHOW OF YOURS...

HUH?!

IT'S GOING TO...

...HIT THE POLE...

IT'S OUTTA HERE!!

THAT'S ONE MORE POINT FOR THE KICK!

THAT'S OUR MUSASHI...

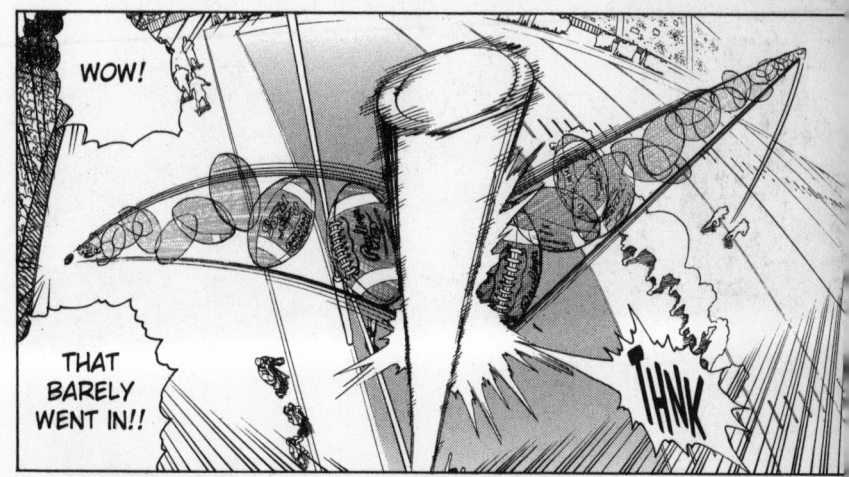

WOW!

THAT BARELY WENT IN!!

THNK

...HIS KICKS ARE EXTREMELY POWERFUL, BUT VERY ROUGH...

AS ALWAYS...

IT WENT IN, DIDN'T IT?

THAT WAS TOO CLOSE, YOU DAMN OLDIE!!

BONK BONK BABONK

Chapter 144
The Devil Bats' Big Gun

MUSASHI!

MUSASHI!!

I WAS WONDERING ABOUT THAT...

...SOMETHING LIKE THAT!!

MUSA-SHAN!

V-Bowl

Extra down 01

Eyeshield 21 Game, Now on Sale!

...SEIBU'S CHRISTMAS BOWL HAS DISAPPEARED.

NOW THAT WE HAVE ALL OUR CARDS...

SNAP

TWO OF THEM.

WE'RE COUNTING ON YOU!

MUSA-SHI!

JUST MAKE THIS KICK!!

WHOA, SO RELIABLE!

LEAVE IT TO ME.

I'LL GIVE YOU A BIG ONE.

WHOOOA!!

TOUCH-DOWN!!

A SPARTAN PASS THAT TESTS THE RECEIVER'S LIMITS!!

LIKE A LASER BEAM!!

PINPOINT ACCURACY!

TH-THAT WAS...

...HAS TRIPLED THEIR OFFENSIVE STRENGTH...!

THE ADDITION OF THAT HIDDEN CARD...

THAT'S HIRUMA'S STYLE INDEED.

I THINK IT'S ABOUT TIME TO TELL YOU GUYS.

HEH HEH HEH.

THE DEVIL LASER BULLET!!!

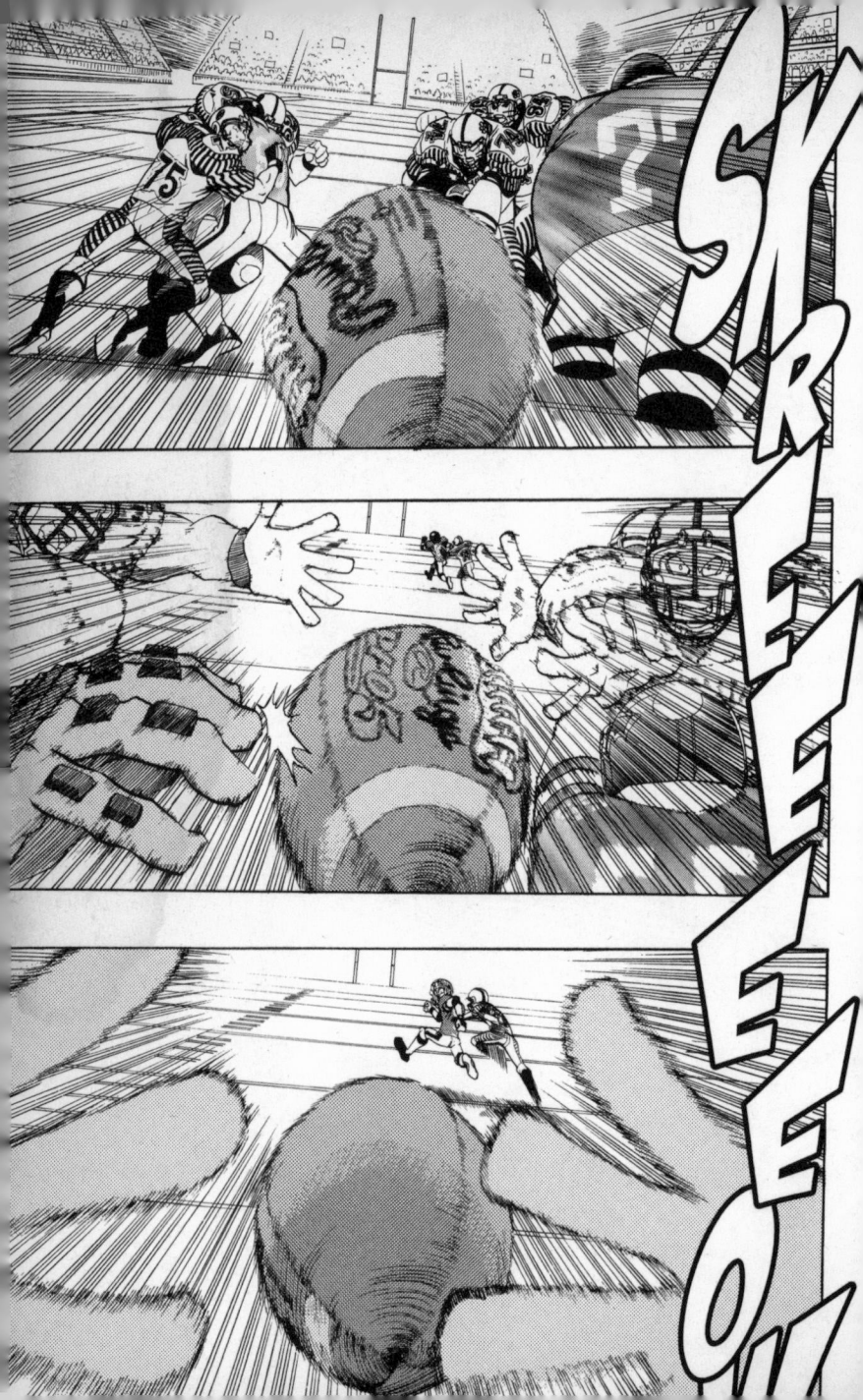

AIR...

...TWIN HORNS!!

SENA...!

DEVIL BAT DIVE?!

A BIT UNEXPECTED... ...BUT NOT ENOUGH!!

DIVING OVER THE TOP FOR ONLY A BALL'S LENGTH?

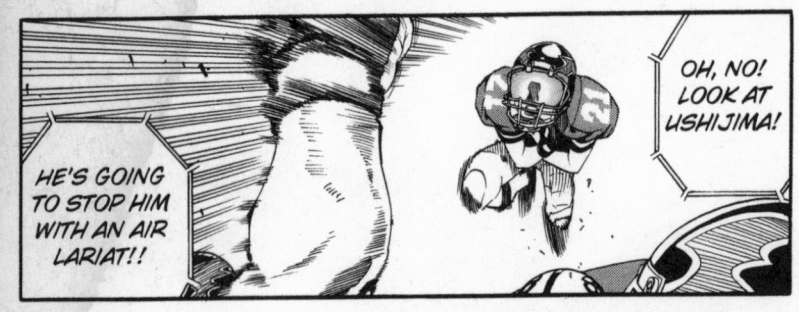

OH, NO! LOOK AT USHIJIMA!

HE'S GOING TO STOP HIM WITH AN AIR LARIAT!!

HUH?

HE... ...SLOWED DOWN...?

...?

50

WHISH

ALL RIGHT, YOU DAMN LINEMEN!

IT'S NOT EVEN THE LENGTH OF THE BALL.

SHOVE IT DOWN THEIR THROATS!!

...JUST A LITTLE FURTHER AND YOU'VE GOT IT.

DEIMON...

OUI OUI

...WE'LL BE ABLE TO ATTACK THREE MORE TIMES, RIGHT?

IF WE CAN ADVANCE ONE MORE STEP...

HEY! THEY'RE COMING ON WITH NO HUDDLE!!

HUT!!

SHIFT SHIFT SHIFT

IT'S A BATTLE OF STRENGTH!

LOCK UP THE CENTER!!

CRUNCH BAN SLA

THREE... I SEE!!

ooo

DID YOU FIGURE SOMETHING OUT?!

WHAT?

OUR ONLY PROBLEM IS TIME.

SIX POINTS FOR EVERY TOUCHDOWN, SO...

IT'S A 20-POINT GAP, RIGHT?

IF WE DON'T SCORE FOUR TOUCHDOWNS IN THE SECOND HALF, WE CAN'T WIN.

LET'S SEE... FOUR TIMES?

Without Kicks

20-Point Difference

With Kicks

THAT MEANS A TOUCHDOWN WILL BE SEVEN POINTS AND...

UMM.

WE ONLY NEED THREE TOUCHDOWNS TO CATCH UP!!

KICK

MUSASHI'S COME BACK SO...

...FROM THE KICK AFTER THE TOUCH-DOWN.

...WE CAN GET ONE BONUS POINT...

EVERYBODY ALREADY KNEW THAT ...

WELL ...

... YEAH.

THEY'RE MEASURING THE DISTANCE NOW.

LOOK, SUZUNA.

IS IT OKAY MOVING JUST A LITTLE BIT LIKE THAT?

FOUR YARDS IS LIKE AS LONG AS THIS BENCH, RIGHT?

FOUR-YARD GAIN!!

HUH?

FIRST DOWN!

...ADVANCED A TOTAL OF TEN YARDS.

DEIMON DEVIL BATS...

...WE CAN KEEP ATTACKING.

...IF WE MOVE TEN YARDS EVERY THREE DOWNS...

EVEN THOUGH WE'RE ADVANCING LITTLE BY LITTLE...

BA-ROOM

IF THEY CAN'T STOP KURITA...

...JUST LIKE A MOVING FORTRESS...

...WE'LL JUST KEEP MOVING FORWARD FOREVER...!

ROAWR!!

MY WHOLE BODY'S ALREADY...

OW, OW, OW!!

OUCH.

THAT BULL-DOZING DRIVE IN THE CENTER...

...JUST WON'T STOP!!

DEIMON'S AMAZING!

CRASH BANG CRUNCH

Chapter 143
DEVIL LASER BULLET

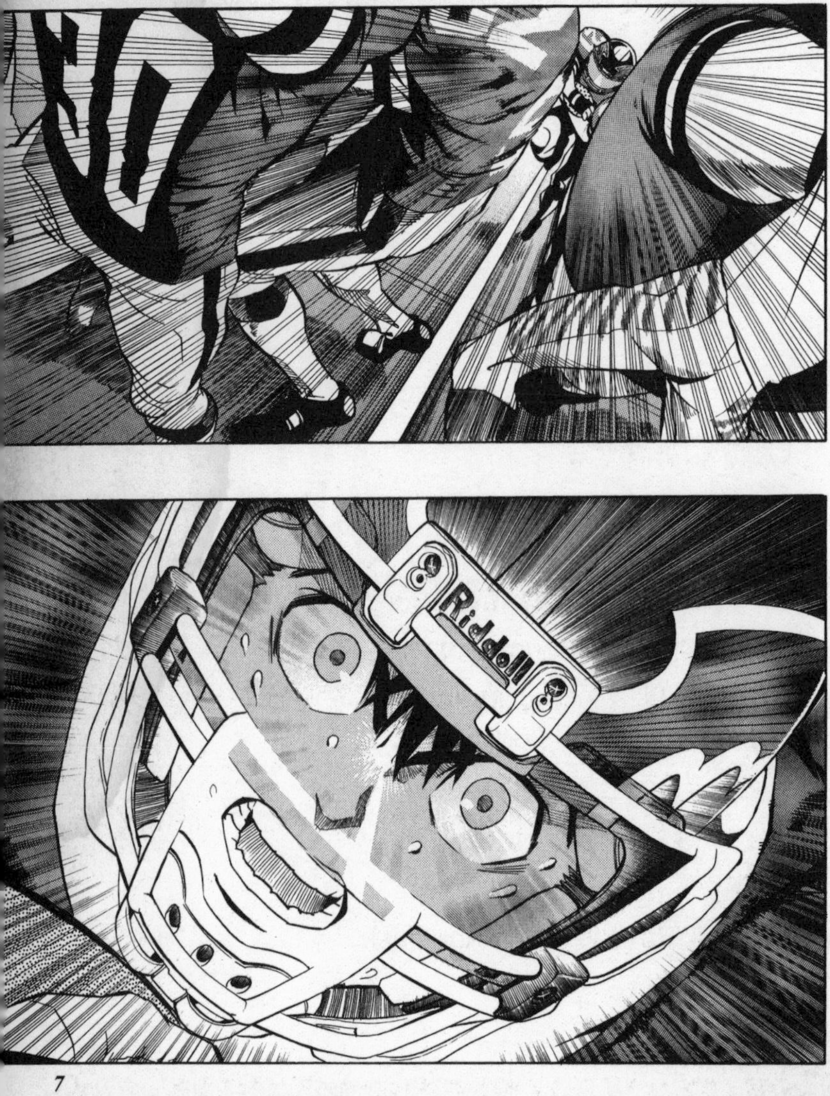

Vol. 17:
The Drive to Be the Best

CONTENTS

Sena Kobayakawa is a shy kid in his first year of high school. To reinvent himself, he joins the school football team. When his exceptional running ability comes to light, he is forced to compete under an assumed identity, "Eyeshield 21."

The goal is winning the Christmas Bowl! With their eyes set on the task, Deimon moved into the Fall Tournament. Showing the fruits of their training in America, Deimon made it into the semifinals, but their opponent, said to be the strongest in Tokyo, is the Seibu Wild Gunmen! The Gunmen's devastating offensive power left Deimon 20 points behind in the first half. But with Musashi's last-minute miraculous comeback, all the members of Deimon have finally joined together to counterattack!!

The Story So Far

THE PLAYERS

TETSUO ISHIMARU

YOICHI HIRUMA

THE KID
(SHIEN MUSHANOKOJI)

RYOKAN KURITA

JO TETSUMA

MUSASHI (GEN TAKEKURA)

DAIKICHI KOMUSUBI

BUFFALO USHIJIMA

KOTARO SASAKI

NATSU-HIKO TAKI

DOBUROKU SAKAKI

MACHINE-GUN SANADA

KUMABU-KURO

KAZUKI JUMONJI

KOJI KUROKI

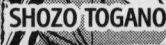
SHOZO TOGANO